THE ULTIMATE THYROID DIET COOKBOOK

THE BEST BEGINNER'S GUIDE. DISCOVER NEW RECIPES TO BOOST YOUR THYROID HEALTH AND FIX YOUR BROKEN METABOLISM

Table of Contents

Introduction 8
Chapter 1.   The Thyroid 10
   What Is the Thyroid, and What Role Does It Play? 10
   What Happens When It Isn't Working Correctly? 10
   Common Thyroid Conditions 10
      Thyroiditis 11
      Subacute Thyroiditis 11
      Graves' Disease 11
      Goiter 12
      Thyroid Nodule 12
      Thyroid Storm 13
      Hashimoto's Thyroiditis 14
      Hyperthyroidism 15
      Thyroid Cancer 17
   Thyroid Tests and Treatment, When Should You See Your Doctor? 18
      Common Tests and Treatments 19
Chapter 2.   Thyroid Diet for Weight Loss 20
   Thyroid Exercise for Upper Body 21
      Cardio Warm-Up 21
      Normal Crunches 21
      Bicycle Crunches 22
      Resistance Crunches 22
      Belly Dancing 22
      Running Uphill 22

Push-Ups	23
Mountain Climbers	23
Weights	23
Exercises for Lower Body	24
Squats	24
Stepping	24
Leg Raises	24
Running Downhill	25
Skipping	25
Cross Fit Training	25
Nutrition	25
Alternate Therapies	26
Supplements	26
Meditation	26
Guided Visualization	26
Yoga	27
Crystal Healing	27
Acupressure	27
Acupuncture	28
Aroma Therapy/ Music Therapy	28
Massages	28
Chapter 3. Breakfast Recipes	30
1. Easy Asparagus Quiche	30
2. Zucchini Bacon Bake	31
3. Baked Breakfast Frittata	32

4. Cauliflower Breakfast Casserole 34

5. Sausage Breakfast Casserole 35

6. Jalapeno Breakfast Casserole 37

7. Sausage Ricotta Cheese Casserole 38

8. Easy Cheese Egg Bake 40

Chapter 4. Lunch Recipes 41

9. Mussels Mariniere 41

10. Marinated Tuna Steak 42

11. Maple Salmon 44

12. Marinated Grilled Shrimp 45

13. Shrimp Scampi 46

Chapter 5. Vegan & Vegetarian Recipes 48

14. Quinoa Porridge 48

15. Channa Saag 49

16. Portobello Mushroom and Beans 51

Chapter 6. Dinner Recipes 53

17. Paleo Chicken Soup 53

18. Split Pea Soup 55

19. Black Bean Chili 56

20. Pasta Fagioli 57

Chapter 7. Appetizers 60

21. Strawberry Pineapple Chicken Bites 60

22. Deviled Eggs 61

23.	Strawberry Bruschetta	62
24.	Spicy Chicken Wings	63
25.	Shrimp Scamp	64

Chapter 8. Meat Recipes 67

26.	Slow-Cooked Barbecued Beef	67
27.	Grilled Lamb Chops	69
28.	Reduced-Fat Meatballs	71
29.	Stuffed Banana Peppers	73
30.	Pot Roast with Root Vegetables	75

Chapter 9. Chicken & Poultry Recipes 77

31.	Corn and Salsa Chicken Salad	77
32.	Chicken, Penne, and Asparagus Salad	78
33.	Chicken Salad Adobo	80
34.	Butterflied Cornish Hens with Crushed Pepper and Garlic	82
35.	Easy Chicken Lasagna	84

Chapter 10. Salads and Smoothies 86

36.	Mediterranean Greek Cucumber Salad	86
37.	Carrot and Apple Slaw	87

Chapter 11. Drinks 89

38.	Green Dream Hemp Seed Smoothie	89
39.	Non-dairy Coconut Milk Yogurt (Homemade)	90
40.	Shamrock Shake	91

Chapter 12. Top Superfood Recipes for the Brain 93

41. Frozen Berry Yogurt 93

42. Baked Salmon 94

43. Avocado Egg Nests 96

44. Super Green Tea Smoothie 98

45. Dark Chocolate Cake 99

Chapter 13. Top Superfood Recipes for Thyroid Health 101

46. Soy Slow Cooked Ribs with Snap Peas 101

47. Cauliflower Rice with Sautéed Peppers and Onions 103

Chapter 14. Side Dishes and Desserts 105

48. Green Juice Popsicles 105

49. Brazil Nut Brownies 106

50. Banana Sushi 108

51. Mango Fruit Tart 109

Introduction

Have you ever wondered what the thyroid is and what function it has in your body? Maybe you have heard people talking about their struggles to lose weight because of their thyroid or that they are always tired? Whether you know a lot about your thyroid or it's a brand new topic, this book will help you learn more about the thyroid and its effect on your body and weight. Although it is small in size, It performs a number of functions and vitally influences almost the entire body.

You may be surprised to learn that it regulates carbohydrate and fat metabolism, body temperature, respiration, brain development, the nervous system and the heart, levels of blood, calcium, cholesterol, skin integrity, and menstrual cycles. It even produces hormones with the help of iodine. When the thyroid does not function properly, a number of disorders occur. It may become underactive and produce fewer hormones. This condition is referred to as hypothyroidism in the US. It is caused due to autoimmune thyroiditis or Hashimoto's disease. A person may gain weight due to this ailment, and if left untreated, causes symptoms to become exacerbated.

On the other hand, the thyroid may become overactive and start producing excessive hormones. This is known as hyperthyroidism. It hastens all the actions that take place within the body. That means the metabolic rate increases, the heart starts palpitating, and blood pressure levels rise. If this condition is not treated, it can lead to a thyroid storm, which can be fatal.

This small gland also has a connection with the gut and the liver. The health of the thyroid is closely related to the well-being of these organs. If your liver or guts are not healthy, then there is an impact on thyroid functioning and vice versa.

Besides medication, a person can ensure that their thyroid remains healthy by adopting a suitable diet and lifestyle. However, while there is no specific diet for the thyroid, eating the right foods with the appropriate nutrients can contribute to the thyroid's wellness. You can include various activities such as yoga and meditation to keep the hormone levels normal. Doing low-impact aerobic exercises as part of your daily routine is also a great way to keep this fantastic gland in good shape.

This book has been created to help you use food to create a healthy gut, which will help you take care of your thyroid.

By the time you reach the end of this book, you'll have all the information you need to improve and maintain your thyroid health. If you're ready to learn more about the thyroid, then let's begin.

Chapter 1.   The Thyroid

What Is the Thyroid, and What Role Does It Play?

The thyroid is an important gland located in the neck in front of a person's windpipe or trachea. It has a butterfly shape with two lobes on the right and left side, which is joined by a patch of tissue known as the isthmus. It secretes hormones that influence the growth, development, metabolism, and temperature of the body. There are two key hormones secreted: triiodothyronine (T3) and thyroxine (T4).

T4 is converted to T3, which is more active. Thyroid hormones are responsible for regulating the metabolic rate, and they affect the energy levels and weight of an individual.

Another key hormone is calcitonin, which helps in maintaining calcium balance. There is a well-organized feedback system that regulates the production of thyroid hormones. A gland situated below the brain, known as the pituitary gland, is also involved in this process (The American Association of Endocrine Surgeons, n.d.).

What Happens When It Isn't Working Correctly?

When the gland does not function properly, all the hormones and functions mentioned earlier get disrupted. This can lead to thyroid diseases that encompass a wide variety of issues. The thyroid may become underactive, which is known as hypothyroidism. It might become overactive for different reasons and lead to a condition known as hyperthyroidism. The gland may become enlarged, called a goiter, and sometimes there may be tiny lumps in the gland known as nodules. There are many other possible thyroid conditions.

Common Thyroid Conditions

Let's take a look at some of the most common thyroid conditions below:

Thyroiditis

This is a common term that refers to the inflammation of a person's thyroid. It includes a number of disorders that cause thyroid inflammation, which is presented in various ways.

For instance, in the U.S., the most prevalent reason for hypothyroidism is Hashimoto's thyroiditis (American Thyroid Association, n.d.).

Postpartum thyroiditis causes thyrotoxicosis (high levels of thyroid hormone in the blood) temporarily that is followed by hypothyroidism, which is also of a temporary nature. This thyroid issue usually occurs after the baby is delivered (American Thyroid Association, n.d.).

Subacute Thyroiditis

Subacute thyroiditis is the main cause of thyroid pain. Moreover, thyroiditis also occurs in patients who take certain drugs like amiodarone and interferon.

Subacute Thyroiditis Treatment

The pain that occurs due to inflammation can be cured by taking aspirin or acetaminophen. If these fail to provide any relief, the doctor may ask you to take anti-inflammatory medicines like dexamethasone or prednisone for some time.

Graves' Disease

Grave's disease is another common disorder affecting Americans. It was first described by a doctor a century and a half ago and named after him. In the U.S., it is the most popular reason for the development of hyperthyroidism and occurs in about 1 out of 200 people (Wallace and Kinman, 2017). It is a type of autoimmune disorder.

This disease occurs when the immune system of the body mistakenly attacks a person's thyroid gland. Due to this, the gland can start producing excessive amounts of the hormone that regulates metabolism.

Graves' disease is hereditary and can develop at any time. However, it usually develops between the ages of 20-30 in women. Stress, smoking, and pregnancy are some risk factors (Wallace and Kinman, 2017).

It can be diagnosed with a physical exam that can reveal high levels of blood pressure, rapid pulse, enlarged thyroid, and bulging eyes. If it is not treated, it may lead to brittle bones and heart problems.

Goiter

A goiter is an enlargement of a person's thyroid gland and is noncancerous by nature. A deficiency of iodine in the regular diet is the most frequent cause of goiter. It has been estimated that 800 million people have an iodine deficiency, and out of that, 200 million have a goiter (Wallace and Kinman, 2017).

Conversely, in the US, where people use iodized salt and get sufficient iodine, a goiter is sometimes a sign of, or caused by, hyperthyroidism (Wallace and Kinman, 2017).

Anyone can have a goiter, and its incidence is not limited to a particular age group. But it is more common in women whose age is more than 40 years. Goiters can also run in the family, so if previous generations have had goiters, it's more likely for the next generations to have them too. Besides this, the use of certain medications, radiation exposure, and pregnancy are some other risk factors.

Thyroid Nodule

Sometimes tiny lumps grow within the gland, which are referred to as thyroid nodules. In countries that are iodine-sufficient, about 5% of women and 1% of men have big enough nodules to be felt. Nearly 50% of the people have very tiny nodules that cannot be detected by touch (Wallace and Kinman, 2017).

The causes of these nodules are not always known. They can develop due to Hashimoto's disease or iodine deficiency. They may be filled with fluid or may be solid.

Most of them are benign. However, in some cases, they can be cancerous. Generally, they do not lead to any symptoms. But if they are large, there may be swelling in the neck, and you may have difficulty swallowing and breathing. Other complications include pain and an increased risk of goiter (Wallace and Kinman, 2017).

To find and examine nodules, a doctor may check them by doing an ultrasound test. If it has to be examined further, they may do a biopsy.

Thyroid Storm

Thyroid storm is a hazardous health condition that is associated with undertreated or untreated hyperthyroidism. It is characterized by extremely high levels of blood pressure, body temperature, and heart rate. The situation can be very dangerous and may be fatal if treatment is not prompt and aggressive (Moore, 2017).

A thyroid storm may develop in people who have hyperthyroidism after they experience any of these:

- Stroke
- Surgery
- Trauma
- Serious emotional stress
- Pulmonary embolism
- Heart failure
- Diabetic ketoacidosis

The symptoms of a thyroid storm are the same as the symptoms of hyperthyroidism. However, they are usually much more severe and sudden. It is a life-threatening event, unlike general hyperthyroidism. For example, in hyperthyroidism, a person may experience a rapid heart rate, but during a thyroid storm, their heart rate can increase so dramatically that it can be fatal (Moore, 2017).

Hashimoto's Thyroiditis

In the US, Hashimoto's disease or chronic lymphocytic thyroiditis is the most popular reason for hypothyroidism. Nearly 14 million people in America are currently diagnosed with this disease (Wallace and Kinman, 2017).

Although its occurrence is not associated with any particular age, it is more prevalent amongst women belonging to the middle-aged group (Wallace and Kinman, 2017).

Symptoms

If the disease is mild, the symptoms are not obvious. The condition can be stable for many years. The symptoms are subtle and not specific, so they mimic the symptoms of various other conditions. The signs include:

- Depression
- Fatigue
- Slight weight gain
- Constipation
- Dry, thin hair
- Dry skin
- Intolerance towards cold
- Irregular and heavy menstruation
- Puffy, pale face
- Enlarged thyroid gland or goiter

Causes

Hashimoto's occurs when the body's immune system attacks the thyroid gland and destroys it, making it incapable of producing hormones.

Risk Factors

The factors that increase the likelihood of getting the disease include:

- Sex: women have a greater tendency to get this disease compared to men.

- Age: even though the disease can develop at any time, it usually occurs in middle-aged people.

- Radiation exposure: If a person is exposed to very high radiation levels in the environment, the chances of getting this disease increases.

- Heredity: a person is at a greater risk of getting the disease if other family members have any autoimmune diseases or thyroid disorder.

- Any autoimmune disease: those people who have any autoimmune diseases like lupus, type 1 diabetes, or rheumatoid arthritis are more susceptible to get Hashimoto's disease.

Hyperthyroidism

Hyperthyroidism occurs when the gland becomes overactive and produces excessive quantities of hormones. It is not very common in men and affects about 1% of women (Wallace and Kinman, 2017).

Hypothyroidism Treatment

A person with hypothyroidism has to take synthetic hormones like levothyroxine to replace the natural thyroid hormones throughout life.

Symptoms

The symptoms of hyperthyroidism include:

- Anxiety

- Nervousness
- Restlessness
- Racing heart
- Increased sweating
- Irritability
- Shaking
- Difficulty in sleeping
- Brittle nails and hair
- Thin skin
- Muscle weakness
- Bulging eyes
- Weight loss

How it Affects Your Metabolism

Thyroid hormones regulate metabolism. A person's metabolism is the amount of energy their body utilizes and the rate at which it uses energy. So thyroid hormones also affect the body's basal rate of metabolism, or how much energy the body uses at rest.

When the thyroid produces too many hormones, then the basal rate is high. So the body consumes more energy when it is at rest. That is why a person loses weight when they have hyperthyroidism.

Causes

The most important reason for the development of hyperthyroidism is Graves' disease. Multinodular goiter or toxic nodular goiter can also make the gland produce excessive hormones (Wallace and Kinman, 2017).

Risk Factors

Risk factors for hyperthyroidism include:

- Medical history of family members who have or had Graves' disease.

- Women are at a greater risk.

- A person who suffers from chronic illnesses, like type 1 diabetes, is more susceptible to get hyperthyroidism

Hyperthyroidism Treatment

The production of the thyroid hormone can be stopped or slowed down with:

- Radioactive treatment: in this form of treatment, you are given radioactive iodine in the form of a liquid dose or tablet. The iodine damages the thyroid gland's cells so that they cannot produce hormones.

- Anti-thyroid medicines: they may help to get rid of the symptoms within 6 to 8 weeks. But you may have to take the medication for a year and have regular checkups to ensure that the hormone levels are stable and balanced.

- Surgery: This option is used only if other medical options don't work. After surgery, you'll have to take additional medications to make up for the lack of thyroid hormone production.

Thyroid Cancer

Thyroid cancer is not very common, and most of the cases may be cured. There are different types of thyroid cancers, such as papillary, follicular, medullary, anaplastic, and thyroid lymphoma. The treatment depends on the type of cancer (Thyroid cancer, n.d.).

Symptoms

Thyroid cancer typically doesn't show any symptoms in the early stages. In the advanced stages, the following symptoms may be visible:

- A lump on the neck that can be identified by touching that area.

- Changes in a person's voice, including increased hoarseness.

- Pain in the throat or neck.
- Difficulty in swallowing.
- Lymph nodes become swollen.

Causes

The cause of thyroid cancer is not known. The disease occurs when genetic changes or mutations take place in the cells present in the thyroid. The mutations give the cells a chance to multiply and grow quickly, and thus, cannot die like normal cells. These abnormal cells get accumulated and form tumors. As a result, they may invade nearby tissues and spread to other parts of the body (Thyroid cancer, n.d.).

Risk Factors

Factors that increase the chances of its occurrence are:

- Sex: it affects more women than men.
- Genetic syndromes: for example, multiple endocrine neoplasias and familial medullary thyroid cancer are inherited genetic syndromes.
- Exposure to severe radiation: for example, exposure to radiation during accidents in nuclear power plants, weapons testing, or radiation treatments are done for the neck or head.

Thyroid Cancer Treatment

Thyroid cancer can be treated by removing the cancerous tissue or gland using a thyroidectomy procedure.

Thyroid Tests and Treatment, When Should You See Your Doctor?

If you notice any of the symptoms that have been mentioned, you should consult your doctor or healthcare provider to get a full evaluation of your health.

The doctor will take your medical history, background, and thyroid condition into consideration and decide the tests and treatment accordingly.

Common Tests and Treatments

A number of tests and treatments are used for adjusting the hormone levels. Besides medicine and surgery, there are various means of getting relief from the discomfort and helping the gland function better, such as herbal remedies, diet supplements, and specific exercises. We will take a look at some of these later in this book.

- Blood Tests

The doctor can use blood tests to determine the level of hormones present in a person's blood. The tests show the amount of thyroid hormone and also the hormone released by the pituitary gland, which stimulates the thyroid (TSH).

When a person has hypothyroidism, TSH levels are higher because the body prompts the thyroid to produce more hormones. If the individual has hyperthyroidism, the TSH level is very low, and the thyroid hormone level is high (Diagnosis and treatment of thyroid problems, n.d.).

- Iodine Uptake Test

This test is used for finding the cause of hypothyroidism and tracks the quantity of iodide that the gland absorbs. This mineral is the main component of thyroid hormones, and the body gets it from the food that a person eats. So, if you know the quantity of iodine that is absorbed, you can tell the amount of hormone produced by the gland.

In the next chapter, we will be looking at how the thyroid, gut health, and liver are interconnected.

Chapter 2.   Thyroid Diet for Weight Loss

As has been previously mentioned, people can use the thyroid diet for weight loss. People suffering from hypothyroidism are the main reason for this weight loss diet. Hypothyroidism can cause weight gain. In order to lose weight or at least maintain it at a normal level, experts advise using the specially formulated thyroid diet.

The most effective weight loss program designed for thyroid patients focuses not only on calorie counts but also on spacing caloric intake throughout the day. That is, the calculated calorie intake is taken in several mini-meals.

Also, experts believe that people who suffer from hypothyroidism need to adjust the proportions and distribution of macronutrient intake. A meal should comprise 40% proteins, 35% carbohydrates (from low glycemic index foods), and 25% fats, with 250 to 300 calories at each meal.

Let's take a closer look at the previous example:

A person who weighs 75 kilograms (165 pounds) with a thyroid condition (e.g., hypothyroidism) wants to lose weight safely.

Get the daily calorie needs: 75 kilograms X 25 = 1875 calories per day

Subtract 200 calories (thyroid factor, to account for thyroid condition):

   1875-200= 1675 calories per day for safe weight loss

Divide a day's worth of meals into mini-meals, with 300 calories each meal. To get the number of 300-calorie meals per day, divide the calorie for weight loss by 300:

1675 calories / 300 = 5.58 or 6 mini-meals a day

This means that a person who weighs 75 kilograms would need to eat 6 mini-meals each day, at 300 calories per meal, to lose weight safely. The mini-meals should be evenly spaced out throughout the day.

The recommended rate of weight loss is at 1 kilogram or 2.2 pounds a week only. Going more than that can trigger starvation mode in the body. While the body still has adequate fat and energy stores, abruptly and severely reducing food intake will cause the body to recognize it as going into starvation. Instead of losing weight and burning fats, the body really tries hard to retain all the fats and keep eating. Cravings will become over the top in this case, which can lead to serious overeating and gaining back more weight than what was initially lost.

Take it slow and don't do too many things all at once. The idea is to gradually settle into a lifestyle and not rush into anything, no matter how bad a situation is.

So, in order to lose weight effectively and sustainably, lose weight gradually and safely.

Thyroid Exercise for Upper Body

Although exercising, as a whole, is a good way to remain fit, you must concentrate on losing fat in particular areas of your body in order to help your thyroid issue. This chapter looks at several exercises, which will help you feel relaxed and rejuvenate your body completely. We look at exercises aimed at the upper body, which will help you cut the fat out from these specific areas.

Cardio Warm-Up

It is extremely important to indulge in a cardio warm-up. You must get your heart rate up and jump. For this, you must do a small warm-up routine followed by some high-intensity exercise such as getting on the treadmill. You can also hold on to a bar and start jogging in the same place. Getting heart rate high will help you cut out more fat from your body.

Normal Crunches

Normal crunches are great for you to lose fat from your stomach area. They will help in toning the muscles and slice through the fat in your abdomen. To perform these normal crunches, start by lying on the floor on your back and fold your legs. Place your hands behind your head or simply on your tummy. Now without moving your legs, lift your upper torso and make sure that your chin touches your knees. Lie down again and keep repeating this set of exercises.

Bicycle Crunches

Bicycle crunches are a great way to tone your abdominal muscles and obliques. All you have to do is start by lying on your back like you would for your normal crunches. Now place your hands behind your head and lift both legs a little above the ground. Now lift your upper torso and bring your right knee towards your chest. Bend your upper torso from the left and try touching your right knee with your left elbow. Continue this with the other side as well. This bicycle crunch will help you have completely toned muscles in no time.

Resistance Crunches

Resistance crunches will help you build strong lower abs. To perform them, start by lying on the floor and placing your feet on a higher platform. Now place some dumbbells on your stomach and start lifting your lower torso up. You must feel the burn in your stomach and literally feel like all the fat is melting away. Keep doing it and feel the burn in your upper and lower abdomen. It is best to stop when you can't do anymore, or doing around 25 is ideal for beginners.

Belly Dancing

This is a great hobby for women looking to cut the fat from their bellies. That is a problem area for many women, and they often complain about having too much stomach fat. For this, it is best to indulge in an activity such as belly dancing. All you need to do is enroll in a class or do it at home by watching a video. You don't have to wear a belly dancing costume and can do it in normal clothes. Several women love it mainly because it helps them cut out on belly fat without having to indulge in rigorous exercises.

Running Uphill

Running uphill is great for the upper body. This is especially for those looking to cut on some fat present in their hips and obliques. All you have to do is find an uphill road or track and start running on it. This will ensure that your entire body avails a workout, and so your legs. You can keep running uphill and not stop until you cannot run anymore. If there is no uphill track, then running up the stairs is also equally challenging. Do this for around 20 minutes.

Push-Ups

Normal push-ups are recommended for those that cannot indulge in rigorous exercising. Push-ups will help in cutting down the fat from both the belly and the arms. You can do regular push-ups as well as planks. Planks refer to lowering your upper body in order to reach the upper push-up position and then standing back up. This exercise can be slightly more intensive as compared to normal push-ups, and so; it is best that you do the former if you don't have the capacity to take this on. Stop whenever your belly and arms start to ache.

Mountain Climbers

Mountain climbers are for all those that are really determined to cut out the fat from their bodies at the earliest. If you do it every day, then you will easily lose excess weight. To perform this, start by getting yourself in the upper plank position. Now look up and bring your right knee to your chest. Push it back down and bring your left knee to your chest. Push it back down and lift your right knee up again. You must duplicate the action taken by mountain climbers while climbing mountains.

Weights

Lifting weights is always good for your arms. You can cut the flab present in your arms and feel confident. You can choose weights depending on your capacity and use them to lift and tone your arms. You can also use barbells or heavy lifts to tone your biceps and also triceps. It is always best to use barbells and weights after doing push-ups as it will add leverage to it.

These form the various upper body exercises that you can perform and reduce your weight. But remember that you must remain persistent and not stop exercising just because you are feeling tired. The point is to continue exercising when you are tired so that you can burn away the fat by using up all the excess sugars.

Exercises for Lower Body

Your lower body will require just as much of a workout as your upper body. You can't have a well-toned upper body and a fatty lower body. Although some exercises will work on your upper and lower body, you must specifically address some of your lower body issues. Here are some exercises that you can take up to affect your lower body's muscles and get toned calves, thighs, and a firm butt.

Squats

Squats are amazing lower body exercises. You can do normal squats by holding your hands in front of you and sitting down or do splay leg squats, which will help tone your butt. If you have a lot of fat in your hips, then you can do deeper squats and hold weights in your hand to add leverage to your exercise. You can also jump up and down and land in a squat every time you jump down.

Stepping

Stepping refers to climbing up steps and getting down fast in quick succession. Stepping is great for your legs and hips. When you take up stepping, you have the chance to tone both your calves and hips. You can buy a stepper if you like, or simply getting on and getting off the staircase will help you. Take safety precautions, and don't do it too fast lest you hurt yourself. Ideally, walking up and down a flight of stairs around 15 times will work well.

Leg Raises

Leg raises are a great exercise for all those looking to tone their obliques. Lie on the floor and turn to the side. Support your body by placing your upper arm on the floor. Now lift your leg in the air 3/4ths of the way and then lower it again. Don't lower it all the way down and lower it to maintain a gap of a centimeter from the ground. Do 20 repetitions on each side. You can increase the number depending on your capacity.

Running Downhill

Just like running uphill helps you reduce upper body fat, running downhill will work for your lower body and help you cut out on a lot of fat. You must find an incline and run down as fast as you can. Use the same field as you would for your upward run. Keep running downhill and make sure that you remain focused on consciously burning the fat in your body. It is highly possible to add leverage to your workout just by having a mental picture of you running down a track, having lost all your weight, and sporting a slim and trim figure.

Skipping

Skipping is a great lower body fat. All you have to do is skip up and down using either a rope or an imaginary one. Keep skipping until you feel completely tired and can't go on anymore. It is best to keep count and aim at 500 skips in the beginning and slowly increase the number depending on your capacity. You can also do the skipping for a minute and jogging for a minute routine to avail faster and better results.

Cross Fit Training

Cross-fit training is a form of intense exercise that helps cut out the fat from your body. There are several training routines to choose from, and you can take up something fit for your body. These workouts are high intensity, and so you must be prepared to take them up and continue with them and not give up because it is difficult. You can find a partner to work out with you and keep going until you attain your ideal weight.

Apart from these, you can participate in sports activities such as playing basketball or swimming, as they will help you get rid of the fat in your body and increase the production of serotonin. This will effectively cut down on the stress hormone and help you maintain a fit and healthy body and mind.

Nutrition

When you exercise, it is important that you maintain the level of nutrition in your body. Nutrition is important, and you cannot forgo it. Instead of snacking on energy bars, which are loaded with sugar, you can carry fresh fruit and consume it. Similarly, instead of drinking energy drinks, you can drink fruit-infused water. To make some, add cut fruits to a bottle of water and then strain all the fruit out. Carry this with you when you go to a workout. Drink this water every now and then to keep yourself hydrated. In fact, it can replace your fruit juices and also your beverages.

Alternate Therapies

Apart from exercise and medication, there are many things that you can do to avail relief from your third issue. Some generic solutions are mentioned here and can be considered alternate therapies to relieve your thyroid issues.

Supplements

The best alternate therapy is to consume supplements. There are many supplements out there that can be consumed to better your health. Even if you are not interested in treating your thyroid issues directly, it is important that you consume supplements that will be good for your body. You can purchase these online or look for them at local drugstores that stock alternate medicines. Some natural supplements that are good for the thyroid include green tea extracts and nuts and seeds extracts. However, you might have to consult with your physician before you decide to take these up and make sure that they are not tampering with your current medications.

Meditation

Meditation is a great way to cope with the stress that you face. Meditation is nothing but inducing a deep level of trance, which will help you get over your stress and also help you with your thyroid issues. There are many forms of meditational practices to choose from and include walking meditation, breathing exercises, transcendental meditation, etc. The easiest way is to find a quiet spot, sit with folded legs, close your eyes and concentrate on your breath. You can do this twice a day and can be done anywhere, including the office.

Guided Visualization

Guided visualization refers to sending you into a trance but is not completely like hypnotism. The person is hypnotized and sent into a trance state and then asked to imagine that all of his or her troubles, including mental and physical, have disappeared and are now leading a normal life again. This will help the person mentally and also physically. It is a good idea to do this every now and then, and this trance can be easily self-induced and not necessary for someone else to induce it. Just sitting on a relaxing chair and performing this can help the person in a big way.

Yoga

Yoga is an ancient art of performing some predetermines exercises, which help the body and mind remain healthy. Yoga was introduced million so of years ago, and there is a pose for any illness. All you have to do is look up which ones will help the thyroid and perform the poses. You can do it along with your exercise routine and make it a part of your everyday life. You can also join a yoga group, which will teach you the right poses and have others' company. You can also get a partner to join you, and the two of you can perform the poses together and motivate each other to keep going.

Crystal Healing

Crystal healing is an alternate science and helps in healing the body using colored crystals. These colored crystals or stones are said to contain a lot of positive energy. There are many wheels or chakras that are turning inside your body, and each one corresponds to one organ. There is a wheel inside your throat, which keeps turning, and if there is a disturbance in it, you will suffer from thyroid issues. So it is important to keep this chakra in check. This can be done by placing a colored stone on top of the throat, just below the Adam's apple. You must consult a qualified crystal healer to know exactly which stone or crystal needs to be placed.

Acupressure

Acupressure is a technique that is used to help improve the condition of a person. The acupressurist knows of several pulse points on the body, which he or she stimulated by pressing against it. This will help in stimulating the organs that correspond to those points, and the person will have instant relief. But it is important to consult a professional acupressurist and get a recommendation for him or her through a friend or a relative who has already availed the treatment.

Acupuncture

Just like acupressure, acupuncture works on similar principles. However, the difference is that the former merely stimulates the pulse points by pressing against them, and the latter inserts sharp needles into the pulse points to stimulate them. Just like in the case of acupressure, you must consult a thorough professional. This technique is slightly more effective than the previous one as it is invasive and will help reach the source directly.

Aroma Therapy/ Music Therapy

There are aromatherapy and music therapy for those looking to supplement their treatment and avail relief faster. In the former, the person is made to smell natural scents from essential oils, and in the latter, the person is made to listen to some calming music to avail similar benefits. Both can be done within your house's confines, and you can read on which essential oil suits your thyroid issues. It is best to listen to some soothing music as opposed to something loud and meaningless. You can also carry your headphones to the office and listen to some music from time to time.

Massages

A good massage from time to time can help the person feel calm and relaxed. You can get a professional to come and help you out or also ask a family member to do it. Massaging the back, feet, and neck can help you drive away stress and also feel relaxed. Using a stimulating oil is also a good idea, and you must make sure that all the different pressure points on the body are stimulated when you undergo a massage.

These form just some of the alternative therapies that are available to you, and there can be many others that you can choose from. But make sure you don't take up all at the same time and try and concentrate on just one at a time. If you think something is working well enough, then stick with it instead of moving to another therapy. Don't worry about the costs, as your health is important. Once you start feeling better, you can always choose to get these done at home and not avail of these services from outside sources. If you don't believe in some of these therapies, like crystal therapy, then you can choose not to take it up. Look at other forms like meditation and yoga that are extremely effective and follow a regular schedule so that you get your daily dose. It is always a good idea to have your family and friends support you through your condition and help you recover faster. So ask if anyone from your family is interested in taking part in these activities along with you, so that you have company and can carry on for a long time.

Chapter 3.   Breakfast Recipes

1. Easy Asparagus Quiche

Preparation Time: 10 minutes

Cooking Time: 45 minutes

Servings: 8

Ingredients:

- 10 eggs
- 2 lbs. of asparagus, trimmed and remove ends
- 3 tbsp. of olive oil
- Pepper
- Salt

Directions:

1. Preheat the oven to 425 °F.
2. Arrange asparagus on the baking sheet. Drizzle 1-tablespoon of olive oil over asparagus.
3. Roast the asparagus in the preheated oven for 15 minutes.
4. In a mixing bowl, whisk eggs with remaining oil, pepper, and salt.
5. Transfer roasted asparagus in a quiche pan. Pour egg mixture over asparagus.
6. Bake at 350 °F for 30 minutes or until the egg sets.

7. Slice and serve.

Nutrition:

- Calories: 146kcal
- Fat: 10.9 g
- Carbohydrates: 4.8 g
- Sugar: 2.6 g
- Protein: 9.4 g
- Cholesterol: 205 mg

2. Zucchini Bacon Bake

Preparation Time: 10 minutes

Cooking Time: 30 minutes

Servings: 8

Ingredients:

- 8 egg whites
- 3 tbsp. of bacon, crumbled
- 1/4 cup of unsweetened almond milk
- 3 wedges of Swiss cheese
- 1/2 cup of Cottage cheese
- 2 cups of shredded zucchini

- 1/2 tsp. of salt

Directions:

1. Preheat the oven to 350 °F. Grease 8*8-inch casserole dish.
2. Add shredded zucchini into the prepared dish.
3. Add egg, bacon, milk, Swiss cheese, Cottage cheese, and salt into the blender and blend until smooth.
4. Pour blended egg mixture over shredded zucchini.
5. Bake in the preheated oven for 30 minutes.
6. Serve and enjoy.

Nutrition:

- Calories: 114 kcal
- Fat: 6.4 g
- Carbohydrates: 2.4 g
- Sugar: 0.9 g
- Protein: 11.4 g
- Cholesterol: 19 mg

3. Baked Breakfast Frittata

Preparation Time: 10 minutes

Cooking Time: 35 minutes

Servings: 12

Ingredients:

- 12 eggs
- 1 tsp. of garlic powder
- 2 1/2 cups of mushrooms, chopped
- 1 cup of cheddar cheese, shredded
- 1 red bell pepper, chopped
- 1 small onion, chopped
- 1 cup of ham, chopped
- 1 1/2 cups of asparagus, chopped
- Pepper
- Salt

Directions:

1. Preheat the oven to 375 °F. Grease 9*13-inch-baking pan.
2. Add asparagus, mushrooms, cheese, bell pepper, onion, and ham into the prepared pan.
3. In a bowl, whisk the eggs with garlic powder, pepper, and salt.
4. Pour egg mixture over vegetables and stir gently.
5. Bake for 25-35 minutes or until frittata is set.
6. Slice and serve.

Nutrition:

- Calories: 132 kcal
- Fat: 8.6 g
- Carbohydrates: 3.5 g
- Sugar: 1.8 g
- Protein: 10.8 g
- Cholesterol: 180 mg

4. Cauliflower Breakfast Casserole

Preparation Time: 10 minutes

Cooking Time: 45 minutes

Servings: 6

Ingredients:

- 10 eggs
- 4 cups of cauliflower rice
- 12 oz. of bacon, cooked and crumbled
- 1/2 cup heavy whipping cream
- 1 tsp. of paprika
- 8 oz. of cheddar cheese, shredded
- 1/4 tsp. of pepper

- 1 tsp. of salt

Directions:

1. Preheat the oven to 350 °F. Grease 2-quart casserole dish.
2. Spread cauliflower rice into the prepared dish and top with half cheddar cheese.
3. In a bowl, whisk the eggs with cream, paprika, pepper, and salt and pour over the cauliflower. Top with remaining cheese and bacon.
4. Bake for 45 minutes.
5. Serve and enjoy.

Nutrition:

- Calories: 637 kcal
- Fat: 48.5 g
- Carbohydrates: 6.9 g
- Sugar: 3.5 g
- Protein: 42.5 g
- Cholesterol: 389 mg

5. Sausage Breakfast Casserole

Preparation Time: 10 minutes

Cooking Time: 40 minutes

Servings: 8

Ingredients:

- 12 eggs
- 1 tbsp. of hot sauce
- 3/4 cup of heavy whipping cream
- 2 cups of cheddar cheese, shredded
- 12 oz. of breakfast sausage
- Pepper
- Salt

Directions:

1. Preheat the oven to 350 °F. Grease 9*13-inch casserole dish.
2. Heat a large pan over medium-high heat.
3. Add sausage to the pan and break with a wooden spoon and cook for 5-7 minutes or until meat is no longer pink.
4. Transfer cooked sausage into the prepared dish and spread evenly.
5. In a large bowl, whisk the eggs with hot sauce, cream, cheese, pepper, and salt.
6. Pour egg mixture over sausage and bake for 30-40 minutes.
7. Serve and enjoy.

Nutrition:

- Calories: 391 kcal
- Fat: 32.2 g

- Carbohydrates: 1.2 g
- Sugar: 0.7 g
- Protein: 23.8 g
- Cholesterol: 326 mg

6. Jalapeno Breakfast Casserole

Preparation Time: 10 minutes

Cooking Time: 30 minutes

Servings: 10

Ingredients:

- 12 eggs
- 2 jalapeno peppers, sliced
- 4 oz. of cream cheese, cut into cubes
- 1 cup of cheddar cheese, shredded
- 1/2 cup of bacon, cooked and chopped
- 1 cup of heavy whipping cream
- 1/2 tsp. of pepper
- 1/4 tsp. of salt

Directions:

1. Preheat the oven to 350 °F. Grease 9*13-inch-baking pan and set aside.

2. In a large bowl, whisk the eggs with cream cheese, whipping cream, pepper, salt and pour into the prepared pan.

3. Sprinkle jalapeno slices, bacon, and 3/4 cup of cheddar cheese evenly over the egg mixture.

4. Bake for 25-30 minutes. Remove pan from oven and top with remaining cheese and bake for 5 minutes more.

5. Serve and enjoy.

Nutrition:

- Calories: 209 kcal
- Fat: 17.8 g
- Carbohydrates: 1.5 g
- Sugar: 0.6 g
- Protein: 11 g
- Cholesterol: 238 mg

7. Sausage Ricotta Cheese Casserole

Preparation Time: 10 minutes

Cooking Time: 55 minutes

Servings: 12

Ingredients:

- 10 eggs
- 2 1/2 lbs. of Italian sausage

- 1 tbsp. of fresh basil, chopped
- 12 cherry tomatoes, halved
- 16 oz. of ricotta cheese, cut into cubes
- 4 oz. of cream cheese
- 1 tsp. of salt

Directions:

1. Preheat the oven to 400 °F.
2. Add the sausage into the casserole dish and bake for 20 minutes. Once done, drain the sausage well and break in small pieces using a masher.
3. In a bowl, whisk the eggs with cream cheese until smooth and pour over the sausage. Season with salt. Sprinkle ricotta cheese cubes, tomatoes, and basil on top.
4. Bake for 35-40 minutes more.
5. Serve and enjoy.

Nutrition:

- Calories: 480 kcal
- Fat: 37 g
- Carbohydrates: 7.3 g
- Sugar: 3.7 g
- Protein: 29.1 g
- Cholesterol: 238 mg

8. Easy Cheese Egg Bake

Preparation Time: 10 minutes

Cooking Time: 30 minutes

Servings: 4

Ingredients:

- 4 eggs
- 1/3 cup of half and half
- 4 oz. of cream cheese
- Pinch of salt

Directions:

1. Preheat the oven to 350 °F.
2. Add eggs, half-and-half, cream cheese, and salt into the blender and blend until smooth.
3. Pour the egg mixture into the greased baking dish and bake for 30 minutes.
4. Serve and enjoy.

Nutrition:

- Calories: 188 kcal
- Fat: 16.6 g
- Carbohydrates: 2 g
- Sugar: 0.4 g ; Protein: 8.3 g ; Cholesterol: 202 mg

Chapter 4. Lunch Recipes

9. Mussels Mariniere

Preparation Time: 15 minutes

Cooking Time: 35 minutes

Servings: 4

Ingredients:

- 4 quarts' mussels, debearded and cleaned
- 2 cloves of garlic, minced
- 1 small onion, chopped
- 6 Tbsps. of fresh parsley, chopped
- 1 bay leaf
- 1/4 tsp. of dried thyme
- 2 cups of white wine
- 3 Tbsps. of cream cheese, divided

Directions:

1. Mix the wine, onion, thyme, garlic, 2 Tbsps. of cream cheese, 4 Tbsps. of parsley and bay leaf in a large pot and place over medium heat. Bring to a boil
2. Reduce the heat and simmer for 2 minutes before adding the mussels.
3. After mussels, cook until shells open. This will take about 4-5 minutes

4. Remove mussels, drain liquid, and set aside.

5. Add leftover cream cheese and parsley to the sauce in the pot. Cook until it melts completely.

6. Serve mussels into plates and dribble the prepared sauce over it.

Nutrition:

- Calories: 298kcal
- Carbs: 11g
- Fat: 10g
- Protein: 19g

10. Marinated Tuna Steak

Preparation Time: 40 minutes

Cooking Time: 11 minutes

Servings: 4

Ingredients:

- 4 tuna steaks (4 oz. each)
- 1/4 cup of orange juice
- 1/4 cup of Worcestershire sauce
- 2 Tbsps. of extra virgin olive oil
- 1 Tbsps. of lemon juice
- 2 Tbsps. of fresh parsley, chopped

- 1 clove garlic, minced
- 1/2 tsp. of chopped fresh oregano
- 1/2 tsp. of ground black pepper

Directions:

1. Prepare the marinade by mixing all the ingredients except the tuna in a medium bowl. Mix until well combined, then add the tuna steaks and coat all sides. Leave in the refrigerator for 30 minutes to marinade.
2. While waiting, preheat the grill and lightly oil the grates.
3. Remove tuna and marinade from the refrigerator. Arrange tuna steaks on the grates and grill. Cook for 5 minutes, then turn tuna steaks and coat with marinade. Turn the tuna periodically and baste with marinade until the steak is grilled to the desired level. Discard leftover marinade.
4. Serve.

Nutrition:

- Calories: 200 kcal
- Carbs: 4g
- Fat: 8g
- Protein: 28g

11. Maple Salmon

Preparation Time: 40 minutes

Cooking Time: 20 minutes

Servings: 4

Ingredients:

- 2 Tbsps. of Worcestershire sauce
- 1/4 cup of maple syrup
- 1 clove of garlic, thinly sliced
- 1/8 tsp. of ground black pepper
- 1/4 tsp. of garlic salt
- 1-pound of salmon

Directions:

1. Preheat the oven to 400 °F
2. Mix the syrup, sauce, garlic, pepper, and garlic salt in a small bowl
3. Arrange the salmon in a baking dish and cover it with maple marinade. Cover and keep tuna in the refrigerator for 30 minutes to marinate.
4. Remove salmon from refrigerator and place in the oven to bake for 20 minutes or until it can be flaked with a fork
5. Allow cooling, then serve.

Nutrition:

- Calories: 265 kcal
- Carbs: 14g
- Fat: 12g
- Protein: 23g

12. Marinated Grilled Shrimp

Preparation Time: 35 minutes

Cooking Time: 6 minutes

Servings: 6

Ingredients:

- 3 cloves of garlic, minced
- 1/3 cup of extra virgin olive oil
- 1/4 cup of tomato sauce
- 2 Tbsps. of red wine vinegar
- 2 Tbsps. of fresh basil, chopped
- 1/2 tsp. of salt
- 1/4 tsp. of cayenne pepper
- 2 pounds of fresh shrimp, deveined and peeled
- Skewers

Directions:

1. Preheat the grill.

2. Mix all the ingredients together in a large bowl. Make sure the shrimp is well coated. Cover and keep in the refrigerator for about 30 minutes to 1 hour. Stir only once.

3. Arrange shrimp on skewers by piercing through from the tail to the head. Discard leftover marinade.

4. Lightly oil the grates of the grill and arrange shrimps on it. Grill both sides until shrimp turn opaque. This may take about 5-6 minutes.

5. Serve.

Nutrition:

- Calories: 273 kcal
- Carbs: 3g
- Fat: 7g
- Protein: 41g

13. Shrimp Scampi

Preparation Time: 15 minutes

Cooking Time: 10 minutes

Servings: 6

Ingredients:

- 8 oz. of packaged gluten-free pasta

- 1/2 cup of cream cheese
- 4 cloves of garlic, minced
- 1/4 tsp. of salt
- 1-pound of shrimp, deveined and peeled
- 1 cup of dry white wine
- 1/4 tsp. of ground black pepper
- 3/4 cup of Parmesan cheese
- 1 Tbsps. of fresh parsley, chopped

Directions:

1. Boil the gluten-free pasta and pour it into a colander when ready.
2. Melt the cream cheese in a large saucepan placed over medium heat. Add the shrimp and garlic, fry for 5 minutes or until both sides of the garlic are done.
3. Pour the white wine into the saucepan, add pepper,salt, then boil.
4. Transfer the shrimp to a bowl, then mix with the drained pasta.
5. Serve into plates and garnish with cheese and parsley.

Nutrition:

- Calories: 606 kcal
- Carbs: 36g
- Fat:30g; Protein: 36g

Chapter 5. Vegan & Vegetarian Recipes

14. Quinoa Porridge

Preparation Time: 5 minutes

Cooking Time: 15 minutes

Servings: 4

Ingredients:

- 2 cups of organic quinoa, white
- 1 tsp. of vanilla extract, pure
- 1 tsp. of ground turmeric
- 1 tsp. of ground cinnamon
- 2 cups of coconut milk, preferably unsweetened
- 1/2 tsp. of ground ginger
- 1/8 tsp. of black pepper
- 1/2 cup of canned pears, diced and with juice
- 1/8 tsp. of salt
- 1/4 coconut flakes, preferably unsweetened
- 1/2 cup of golden raisins

Directions:

1. Pour the quinoa into a bowl and rinse under cold water.

2. In a medium-sized saucepan, mix the quinoa and coconut milk and place over medium heat to boil.

3. Once the mixture starts boiling, reduce the heat and cover the saucepan with a tight-fitting lid. Cook for 10-15 minutes until the porridge thickens, and most of the milk is absorbed

4. Remove the pan from heat and add the rest of the Ingredients: turmeric, vanilla, cinnamon, black pepper, ginger, and salt, then stir.

5. For toppings, add pears, coconut flakes, and raisins as desired

Nutrition:

- Calories: 276 kcal
- Carbs: 48g
- Fat: 2g
- Protein: 6g

15. Channa Saag

Preparation Time: 5 minutes

Cooking Time: 12 minutes

Servings: 2

Ingredients:

- 2/3 cup of dried beans
- 1-1/2 cups of cooked no-salt-added garbanzo beans
- 12 oz. of spinach, chopped

- 1 tsp. of ground cinnamon
- 1 tsp. of ground coriander
- 1 tsp. of ground cardamom
- 1 tsp. of garam marsala
- 1 medium onion, thinly sliced
- 2 medium tomatoes, sliced
- 2 cloves of garlic, minced
- 1 tsp. of ginger, grated
- 3 Tbsps. of water

Directions:

1. Add 3 tablespoons of water to a large saucepan, then place on medium heat.
2. Add the onions, ginger, and garlic to the water and cook until tender. This will take about 2 minutes.
3. Add the spinach, spices, and tomatoes. Stir, then allow to cook for 5 minutes.
4. Stir in the cayenne pepper and chickpeas—cook for 5 minutes.
5. Serve.

Nutrition:

- Calories: 298kcal
- Carbs: 53g

- Fat: 4.3g
- Protein: 21g

16. Portobello Mushroom and Beans

Preparation Time: 5 minutes

Cooking Time: 12 minutes

Servings: 2

Ingredients:

- 1 medium onion, thinly sliced
- 2/3 cup of dried beans
- 2 large Portobello mushroom caps, sliced
- 1-1/2 cups of cooked no-salt-added garbanzo beans
- 1 large tomato, sliced
- 2 cloves of garlic, minced
- 1/2 cup of vegetable broth
- 3 Tbsps. of water

Directions:

1. Add 3 tablespoons of water to a large saucepan, then place on medium heat.
2. Add the onions and garlic to the water and cook until tender. This will take about 2 minutes.

3. Add the broth and mushroom. Stir, then allow to cook for 5 minutes until mushrooms become tender.

4. Stir in the garbanzo beans and tomatoes. Reduce the heat and simmer for 5 minutes.

5. Serve.

Nutrition:

- Calories: 143 kcal
- Carbs: 25g
- Fat: 2.1g
- Protein: 11g

Chapter 6. Dinner Recipes

17. Paleo Chicken Soup

Preparation Time: 15 minutes

Cooking Time: 45 minutes

Servings: 4

Ingredients:

- 1 Tbsps. of coconut oil
- 1-pound of ground chicken(organic)
- 2 Tbsps. of sliced ginger
- 1 cup of celery, diced
- 1/2 tsp. of salt
- 1 cup of green onion, sliced with white and green separated
- 3 cups of broth
- 1/2 cup of carrots, shredded
- 1 tsp. of ground turmeric
- 1/16 tsp. of ground turmeric
- 1/4 cup of fresh cilantro, packed
- 14 oz. of full-fat coconut milk
- 1/4 tsp. of red pepper, crushed

Directions:

1. Pour the coconut oil into a large soup pot, then place over medium heat.
2. When the oil starts to sizzle, add the chicken and ginger. Leave to fry for 5-10 minutes.
3. Pour the garlic in and cook for 2 more minutes.
4. Add 1/2 cup of the white part of the green onions and cook for 1 minute.
5. Add the broth, carrots, cinnamon, and turmeric to the mixture in the pot and increase the heat.
6. Once the broth starts boiling, lower the heat, cover the lid and allow it to cook for 20 more minutes. Stir periodically.
7. Add the rest of the green onions (the green part), cilantro, coconut milk, and increase the heat once again. Cook until it boils.
8. After boiling, allow to simmer for 10 minutes.
9. Serve as desired.

Nutrition:

- Calories: 480 kcal
- Carbs: 20g
- Fat: 31g
- Protein: 36g

18. Split Pea Soup

Preparation Time: 8 hours 30 minutes

Cooking Time: 2 minutes

Servings: 6

Ingredients:

- 2 quarts of cold water
- 2-1/4 cups of split peas, dried
- 1-1/2 pounds of ham bone
- 2 medium onions, thinly sliced
- 1 medium potato, diced
- 3 medium carrots, chopped
- 3 stalks of celery, chopped
- 1/4 tsp. of ground black pepper
- 1/3 tsp. of marjoram, dried

Directions:

1. Soak the peas in cold water overnight. Then drain.
2. Boil the soaked peas with marjoram, ham bone, onion, salt, and pepper. Allow to boil, then simmer for 1-1/2 hours. Stir periodically.
3. Remove the ham bone, slice off the meat, chop and return the meat to the broth.

4. Add the potatoes, carrots, and celery. Remove the cover of the pot and continue cooking for about 30-40 minutes.

5. Serve.

Nutrition:

- Calories: 310 kcal
- Carbs: 57.9g
- Fat: 1g
- Protein: 19.7g

19. Black Bean Chili

Preparation Time: 20 minutes

Cooking Time: 1hour 15 minutes

Servings: 6

Ingredients:

- 45 oz. of black beans, undrained
- 14-1/2 oz. of crushed tomatoes
- 1 Tbsps. of extra virgin olive oil
- 1 large onion, sliced
- 2 cloves of garlic, minced
- 1-pound of ground turkey
- 1-1/2 Tbsps. of chili powder

- 1 Tbsps. of dried oregano
- 1 Tbsps. of dried basil leaves
- 1 Tbsps. of red wine vinegar

Directions:

1. Pour the olive oil into a large-sized non-stick pot and place over medium heat. Once the oil starts to sizzle, add the onions and garlic, then stir until onions turn translucent.
2. Add the turkey and fry until the meat turns brown.
3. Add the beans, basil, tomatoes, oregano, chili powder, and vinegar. Lower the heat, cover, and allow to simmer for 60 minutes.
4. Serve.

Nutrition:

- Calories: 366 kcal
- Carbs: 29.6g
- Fat: 9.2g
- Protein: 29.6g

20. Pasta Fagioli

Preparation Time: 10 minutes

Cooking Time: 1hour 30 minutes

Servings: 6

Ingredients:

- 3 Tbsps. of extra virgin olive oil
- 1 large onion, sliced
- 2 cloves of garlic, minced
- 15 oz. of cannellini beans
- 29 oz. of tomato sauce
- 5-1/2 cups of water
- 1 Tbsps. of dried parsley
- 1 tsp. of salt
- 1-1/2 tsp. of dried oregano
- 1-1/2 tsp. of dried basil leaves
- 15 oz. of navy beans
- 1-pound of gluten-free pasta
- 1/3 parmesan cheese, grated

Directions:

1. Pour the olive oil into a large-sized non-stick pot and place over medium heat. Once the oil starts to sizzle, add the onions and garlic, then stir until onions turn translucent.
2. Reduce the heat and stir in the tomato sauce, parsley, basil, cannellini beans, parmesan, navy beans, oregano, salt, and water. Allow simmering for an hour.
3. Boil the pasta in water for 10 minutes; add a pinch of salt, drain, then stir into soup.
4. Serve.

Nutrition:

- Calories: 403 kcal
- Carbs: 68g
- Fat: 7.6g
- Protein: 16.3g

Chapter 7. Appetizers

21. Strawberry Pineapple Chicken Bites

Preparation Time: 20 minutes

Cooking Time: 20 minutes

Servings: 12

Ingredients:

- 2 Tbsps. of extra virgin olive oil
- 2 pounds of shredded chicken
- 12 oz. of strawberry preServings
- 8 oz. of diced pineapples
- 8 oz. of chili sauce
- 1/2 tsp. of salt
- 1/2 ground black pepper
- toothpicks

Directions:

1. Pour the olive oil into a skillet and place it on medium heat. Add in the shredded chicken, and fry for 5 minutes until all sides have turned brown.

2. Lower the heat and add in the strawberry preServings, and chili sauce. Cook for 10 minutes and stir continuously.

3. Add the diced pineapples and season with black pepper and salt. Allow it to cook for 2 minutes.

4. Dish into plates and serve with toothpicks.

Nutrition:

- Calories: 187 kcal
- Carbs: 23.1g
- Fat: 3.8g
- Protein: 15.3g

22. Deviled Eggs

Preparation Time: 10 minutes

Cooking Time: 0 minutes

Servings: 6 (12 deviled eggs halves)

Ingredients:

- 6 hard-boiled eggs, halved
- 1 tsp. of rice wine vinegar
- 1/4 cup of mayonnaise
- 1/2 tsp. of fresh dill, chopped
- 1 tsp. of Dijon mustard
- 1/4 tsp. of garlic powder
- 1/8 tsp. of salt
- 12 fresh dill sprigs

Directions:

1. Carefully remove the egg yolks, and set the egg whites aside.
2. Mash the yolks in a small bowl and mix with mayonnaise, chopped dill, vinegar, mustard, garlic and salt.
3. Scoop the yolk mixture into the egg whites.
4. Garnish each deviled egg with a sprig of dill.
5. Serve or keep in the refrigerator until ready to eat

Nutrition:

- Calories: 139 kcal
- Carbs: 1g
- Fat: 12.3g
- Protein: 6.4g

23. Strawberry Bruschetta

Preparation Time: 10 minutes

Cooking Time: 5 minutes

Servings: 12

Ingredients:

- 24 slices of gluten-free bread
- 2 cups fresh strawberries, chopped

- 1 Tbsps. cream cheese, softened

Directions:

1. Preheat the broiler in the oven to 320 °F.

2. Spread the cream cheese on each slice of bread and arrange it on a large baking sheet

3. Arrange the bread under the broiler until the bread is lightly toasted. This will take about 1-2 minutes.

4. Bring the bread out from under the broiler and arrange the strawberries on the toast.

5. Place the bread back in the oven for about 5 minutes, then serve.

Nutrition:

- Calories: 120 kcal
- Carbs: 23g
- Fat: 1.6g
- Protein: 3.7g

24. Spicy Chicken Wings

Preparation Time: 15 minutes

Cooking Time: 30 minutes

Servings: 12

Ingredients:

- 12 pieces of chicken wings
- 1-1/2 hot sauce
- 1 cup of honey
- 3/4 cup of cream cheese
- 1/3 garlic of salt
- 1/3 tsp. of ground black pepper
- 1 tsp. of cayenne powder

Directions:

1. Preheat the outdoor grill.
2. Lightly oil the grate of the grill, then arrange the chicken on the grill. While periodically turning the chicken, grill for 8-12 minutes.
3. Mix the cream cheese, hot sauce, cayenne pepper, garlic salt, honey, and black pepper in a saucepan, then place on medium heat. Simmer for 10 minutes, then coat the sauce on the grilled chicken wings.

Nutrition:

- Calories: 356 kcal
- Carbs: 23.9g
- Fat: 22.7g
- Protein: 15.6g

25. Shrimp Scamp

Preparation Time: 15 minutes

Cooking Time: 6 minutes

Servings: 4

Ingredients:

- 2 pounds of large shrimp, deveined and peeled
- 6 Tbsps. of unsalted cream cheese, melted
- 1/4 cup of extra virgin olive oil
- 1 Tbsps. of minced garlic
- 1 Tbsps. of minced shallots
- 2 Tbsps. of fresh chives, minced
- Salt, to taste
- 1/2 tsp. of ground pepper
- 1/2 tsp. of paprika

Directions:

1. Preheat the grill to high temperature
2. Mix the cream cheese, garlic, olive oil, chives, shallots, pepper, salt, paprika in a large bowl.
3. Add the shrimp to the mixture and toss to coat it.
4. Lightly oil the grate of the grill.
5. Grill the shrimp, making sure both sides are done before removing them.
6. Serve.

Nutrition:

- Calories: 302 kcal
- Carbs: 0.9g
- Fat: 21.8g
- Protein: 25g

Chapter 8. Meat Recipes

26. Slow-Cooked Barbecued Beef

Preparation Time: 5 minutes

Cooking Time: 8 hours

Servings: 8

Ingredients:

- 1-1/2 pounds of extra-lean ground beef (93% lean)
- 2 Tbsps. of extra-virgin olive oil
- 2 Tbsps. of prepared mustard
- 1 cup of low-sodium ketchup
- 1 small green bell pepper, chopped
- 3 Tbsps. of vinegar

- 1/2 tsp. of ground garlic

- 1 Tbsps. of Worcestershire sauce

- 1 medium onion, chopped

- 1 tsp. of chili powder

Directions:

1. Pour the olive oil into a medium skillet and place over medium heat. Once the oil starts to sizzle, add the onions and beef, then brown the beef.

2. Pour the rest of the ingredients into a slow cooker. Stir.

3. Add the beef and onions. Stir. Cook on high for 3-4 hours or low for 6-8 hours.

4. Serve as burgers or sandwiches.

Nutrition:

- Calories: 249 kcal

- Carbs: 12g Fat: 6g

- Protein: 17g

27. Grilled Lamb Chops

Preparation Time: 120 minutes

Cooking Time: 10 minutes

Servings: 4

Ingredients:

- 2-1/2 pounds of chopped lamb
- 1 tsp. of lemon juice
- 1 small lemon
- 2 tsp. of parsley
- 1 Tbsps. of Dijon mustard
- 2-1/2 Tbsps. of salt

- 1 tsp. of thyme leaves
- 2 Tbsps. of oregano
- 2 Tbsps. of canola oil
- 3 cloves of garlic
- 2 Tbsps. of black pepper
- 3 tsp of extra virgin olive oil

Directions:

1. Preheat the grill to 400 °F.
2. Mix the mustard, thyme, parsley, salt, 1-tablespoon of oregano, pepper, garlic, olive oil, lemon juice in a medium bowl and stir thoroughly. Set aside one-third of the lemon mixture.
3. Place the lamb in a large baking dish, then pour two-third of the lemon mixture on it. Ensure the lamb is well coated. Allow it to marinate in the refrigerator for about 2 hours.
4. Coat the grate of the grill with canola oil. Remove the lamb from the liquid and grill both sides equally for about 10 minutes.
5. Pour the rest of the lemon mixture on the lamb and leave for 5 minutes, then remove.
6. Coat the chops with the leftover oregano. Serve with lemon wedges.

Nutrition:

- Calories: 214kcal
- Carbs: 1g

- Fat: 12g

- Protein: 23g

28. Reduced-Fat Meatballs

Preparation Time: 5 minutes

Cooking Time: 1 hour

Servings: 6

Ingredients:

- 1-1/2 pounds of extra-lean ground beef (93% lean)

- 6 oz. no-salt-added tomato paste

- 3 medium eggs

- 1/2 tsp. of ground garlic powder

- 1/2 Tbsps. of dried oregano
- 1 Tbsps. of dried parsley
- 4 slices of bread, crumbled
- 2 medium onions, chopped
- 1/2 cup of Parmesan cheese, grated
- 1/2 cup of red wine vinegar
- 1/4 cup of water

Directions:

1. Preheat the oven to 375 °F.
2. Mix the beef, cheese, eggs, garlic, oregano, parsley. Whisk well. Add the bread crumbles and form 1-ich meatballs. Arrange the meatballs in a baking pan and bake for 30-40 minutes. Turn only once while baking.
3. Sauté onions in a large skillet, then add tomato paste, vinegar, and water. Cook for 5 minutes, then remove from heat.
4. Serve meatballs with tomato sauce. Garnish with fresh parsley (optional).

Nutrition:

- Calories: 457 kcal
- Carbs: 28g
- Fat: 12g
- Protein: 32g

29. Stuffed Banana Peppers

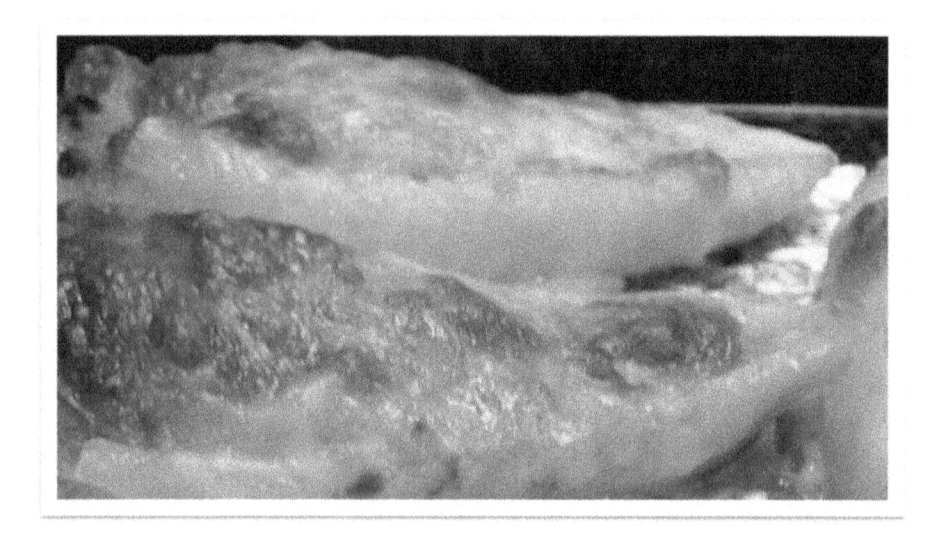

Preparation Time: 10 minutes

Cooking Time: 30 minutes

Servings: 6

Ingredients:

- 1/4 cup of all-purpose flour
- 1-pound of extra-lean ground beef (93% lean)
- 12 banana peppers, hot or sweet
- 1 small onion, thinly sliced
- 1 medium egg
- 1/2 cup of Swiss cheese, grated
- 1/4 tsp. of black pepper

- 1/4 tsp. of vegetable oil.

Directions:

5. Preheat the oven to 350 °F.
6. Prepare the peppers by washing and cutting off the top and bottom.
7. In a medium skillet, brown the beef and onions. This will take about five minutes. When ready, stir in the cheese.
8. Stuff the beef and cheese mixture into the peppers. Set aside.
9. Pour flour on a chopping board.
10. Mix the egg and black pepper in a separate bowl. Dip the peppers into the egg and then roll in flour to coat. Dip into the egg a second time, and then coat in flour again.
11. Coat a baking dish with oil and arrange the peppers in it. Bake for 20 minutes, then remove when the cheese is melted, and flour coating turns brown.

Nutrition:

- Calories: 372 kcal
- Carbs: 19g
- Fat: 9g
- Protein: 30g

30. Pot Roast with Root Vegetables

Preparation Time: 5 minutes

Cooking Time: 2 hours

Servings: 8

Ingredients:

- 2-pound of beef roast
- 4 turnips, peeled and cut into quarters
- 1 medium onion, chopped into quarters
- 4 potatoes, chopped into quarters
- 6 carrots, chopped
- 2 cups of no-salt-added canned tomatoes

- 2 cups of low-sodium beef broth
- 1 parsnip, sliced

Directions:

1. Preheat the oven to 350 °F.
2. Mix all the ingredients together in a large roasting pan. Place the pan in the oven and bake for 2 hours. Check if the meat is tender. If not, bake for 15 more minutes.
3. Serve.

Nutrition:

- Calories: 527 kcal
- Carbs: 41g
- Fat: 22g
- Protein: 40g

Chapter 9. Chicken & Poultry Recipes

31. Corn and Salsa Chicken Salad

Preparation Time: 5 minutes

Cooking Time: 10 minutes

Servings: 4

Ingredients:

- 4 chicken breast halves
- 1/2 cup of salsa verde
- 2 Tbsps. of balsamic vinegar
- 8 fat-free tortilla chips, crushed
- 1 tsp. of brown mustard
- 1 Tbsps. of Cajun seasoning powder
- 1 tomato, sliced
- 2 Tbsps. of fresh cilantro, chopped
- 2 cups of fresh corn kernels
- 1 small avocado, peeled, pitted, and chopped
- 4 scallions, chopped
- Non-stick spray

Directions:

1. Season the chicken with Cajun seasoning powder.

2. Place a large skillet over medium heat and coat with non-stick spray.

3. Place the chicken in the skillet and cook until both sides turn brown. This will take about 5 minutes for each side.

4. Cut each chicken into 4 slices, keeping the slices joined at one end.

5. Prepare the dressing by mixing the salsa verde, 1 Tbsps. of cilantro, vinegar, and mustard in a bowl.

6. Prepare the salad by mixing the scallions, avocados, tomatoes, corn, and leftover 1 Tbsps. of cilantro in a large bowl. Dribble the dressing over it and toss.

7. Serve the salad into 4 plates with a chicken on each plate.

Nutrition:

- Calories: 269 kcal
- Carbs: 24g
- Fat: 8g
- Protein: 29g

32. Chicken, Penne, and Asparagus Salad

Preparation Time: 5 minutes

Cooking Time: 30 minutes

Servings: 4

Ingredients:

- 1/2-pound of chicken breasts, cut into strips
- 2 tsp. of poultry and meat seasoning
- 1-pound of gluten-free pasta
- 1-pound of asparagus, chopped
- 2 medium tomatoes, sliced
- 1 cup of fresh basil, chopped
- 1/4 cup of Pecorino Romano cheese, grated
- 2 cloves of garlic, minced
- 1 Tbsps. of extra virgin olive oil
- 1/4 tsp. of salt
- Non-stick spray

Directions:

1. Rub the chicken with the seasoning.
2. Place a large skillet over medium heat and coat with non-stick spray
3. Place the chicken in the skillet and cook until both sides turn brown. This will take about 5 minutes for each side.
4. Boil the pasta on another burner. Add salt if desired. Once ready, drain the pasta into a colander and reserve the cooking water. Rinse the drained pasta in cold water then transfer it to a bowl
5. In the pasta cooking water, add the asparagus and cook until tender (about 3 minutes). Once done, rinse in cold water and mix with the pasta.

6. In the bowl containing the pasta and asparagus, add the tomatoes, garlic, cheese, oil, salt, basil, and chicken. Toss until well combined.

7. Serve.

Nutrition:

- Calories: 273 kcal
- Carbs: 29g
- Fat: 8g
- Protein: 21g

33. Chicken Salad Adobo

Preparation Time: 5 minutes

Cooking Time: 10 minutes

Servings: 6

Ingredients:

- 1 Tbsps. of orange zest, grated
- 2 Tbsps. of orange juice, squeezed
- 1 Tbsps. of white wine vinegar
- 2 tsp. of extra virgin olive oil
- 1 tsp. of honey
- 1 large tomato, sliced

- 1 tsp. of Dijon mustard
- 1 clove of garlic, minced
- 1 Tbsps. of adobo seasoning
- 1/8 tsp. of salt
- 1 red bell pepper, chopped
- 1-pound of chicken thighs, skinless, deboned, and cut into pieces
- 15-1/2 oz. of black beans, drained and rinsed
- 1 ripe mango, diced
- 1 small red onion, thinly sliced
- 1/2 cup of fresh cilantro, chopped
- 1 jalapeño pepper, seeded and chopped
- Non-stick spray

Directions:

1. Rub the chicken with the adobo seasoning.
2. Place a large skillet over medium heat and coat with non-stick spray.
3. Place the chicken in the skillet and cook until both sides turn brown. This will take about 5 minutes for each side. Remove from skillet and keep in a bowl.
4. Prepare the dressing by mixing the orange juice, orange zest, extra virgin olive oil, vinegar, honey, garlic, mustard, and salt in a small bowl until well combined blended.

5. In the bowl with the chicken, add the mango, beans, bell pepper, tomatoes, cilantro, onions, and jalapeño. Drizzle the dressing over the salad and toss until well combined.

6. Serve.

Nutrition:

- Calories: 248kcal
- Carbs: 23g
- Fat: 8g
- Protein: 21g

34. Butterflied Cornish Hens with Crushed Pepper and Garlic

Preparation Time: 5 minutes

Cooking Time: 30 minutes

Servings: 4

Ingredients:

- 1 Tbsps. of fresh flat-leaf parsley, chopped
- 2 tsp. of extra virgin olive oil non-stick spray
- 1 large clove of garlic, minced
- 1/2 tsp. of salt
- 1/2 tsp. of red pepper flakes

- 3-pound of Cornish game hen

Directions:

1. Preheat the outdoor grill.

2. Lightly oil the grate of the grill with olive oil nonstick spray.

3. Mix all the ingredients (except the Cornish hen) in a small bowl.

4. Prepare the hen by dissecting it with kitchen shears. Cut along both sides of the hens, remove the backbones and discard. Then rub the parsley mixture all over the chicken and under the skin too.

5. Place the hen on the grate and grill for about 30 minutes until both sides are crisp and golden. Remove the hen and place it on a chopping board.

6. Chop the grilled chicken into large pieces. Serve.

Nutrition:

- Calories: 224kcal
- Carbs: 1g
- Fat: 8g
- Protein: 35g

35. Easy Chicken Lasagna

Preparation Time: 5 minutes

Cooking Time: 1 hour 15 minutes

Servings: 9

Ingredients:

- 1-pound of chicken breast, shredded
- 1/2 pound of white mushrooms, thinly sliced
- 26 oz. of fat-free marinara sauce
- 2 large egg whites, lightly whisked
- 16 oz. of part-skim mozzarella cheese, shredded
- 1/4 cup of Parmigiano-Reggiano cheese, grated
- 1/2 tsp. of fresh nutmeg, grated
- 8 oz. of no-salt-added tomato sauce
- 15 oz. of fat-free ricotta cheese
- 9 oz. of no-boil lasagna noodles
- Non-stick spray

Directions:

1. Preheat the oven to 375 °F.
2. Spray the non-stick spray on a large saucepan and place over medium heat. Add the chicken and cook until all sides are lightly browned. This may take 3-4 minutes.

3. Add in the mushrooms. Cook until the liquid comes out or for 5 minutes.

4. Pour in the marina sauce, stir, lower the heat and allow to simmer. Set the pot aside.

5. Mix the mozzarella and ricotta cheese, nutmeg, and egg whites in a small bowl. Set aside.

6. Spread the tomato sauce mixture smoothly on the bottom of a baking pan. Arrange 5 lasagna noodles over the sauce in the first layer. Add 1/3 of the chicken mixture.

7. Repeat step 6 until the ingredients are exhausted. (The ingredients listed above will only make 3 layers).

8. Sprinkle Parmigiano-Reggiano on top of the lasagna, cover, then bake for 45 minutes.

9. Uncover, then bake until the top turns slightly brown. This may take about 10 minutes.

10. Allow cooling for 5 minutes before serving.

Nutrition:

- Calories: 340kcal
- Carbs: 36g
- Fat: 7g
- Protein: 33g

Chapter 10. Salads and Smoothies

36. Mediterranean Greek Cucumber Salad

Preparation Time: 15 minutes

Cooking Time: 0 minutes

Servings: 4

Ingredients:

- 2 medium-size cucumbers, diced
- 1 cup of grape tomatoes
- 1/4 cup of sliced red onion
- 1/2 tsp. of sea salt
- 1/4 tsp. of black pepper
- 1 tsp. of fresh basil, chopped
- 1 tsp. of fresh parsley, chopped
- 1 tsp. of fresh oregano, chopped
- 1 tsp. of minced garlic
- 1 tsp. of red wine vinegar
- 2 tsp. of extra virgin olive oil
- 1/8 tsp. of red pepper, crushed
- 1/2 cup of crumbled feta cheese

Directions:

1. Pour the cucumber, red onions, and tomatoes into a medium-sized bowl and add salt and pepper. Mix all the ingredients and rest for 10 minutes to ensure the maximum blend of the cucumber and tomatoes' juices.

2. After resting, add the basil, oregano, parsley, garlic, vinegar, red pepper, and olive oil. Stir until well combined.

3. Allow to marinate for 5 minutes, then stir. Serve as desired.

Nutrition:

- Calories: 80kcal
- Carbs: 13g
- Fat: 0g
- Protein: 4g

37. Carrot and Apple Slaw

Preparation Time: 5 minutes

Cooking Time: 0 minutes

Servings: 6

Ingredients:

- 10 oz. of shredded carrots
- 4 cups of green apples, cut into matchsticks
- 1/4 cup of mayonnaise

- 1 cup of raisins
- 3 Tbsps. of nonfat Greek yogurt
- 3 Tbsps. of rice vinegar
- 1/2 tsp. of celery seeds
- 1/2 tsp. of salt
- 3 Tbsps. of honey

Directions:

1. In a medium bowl, mix the yogurt, mayonnaise, vinegar, honey, celery, and salt.
2. Add in the carrots, raisins, and apples.
3. Serve with dressing or refrigerate until ready to serve

Nutrition:

- Calories: 236 kcal
- Carbs: 43g
- Fat: 5g
- Protein: 10g

Chapter 11. Drinks

38. Green Dream Hemp Seed Smoothie

Preparation Time: 5 minutes

Cooking Time: 0 minutes

Servings: 4

Ingredients:

- 2 cups of frozen pineapple
- 2 cups of frozen mango
- 2 cups of spinach, packed
- 2 cups of hemp seed milk, homemade
- 1/4 tsp. of coconut extract
- 3 tsp. of hemp seed, hulled

Directions:

1. Put the frozen mango, spinach, pineapple, coconut extract, hemp seed, and hemp seed and the milk into a high-speed blender.
2. Blend until completely smooth.
3. Serve as desired.

Nutrition:

- Calories: 260 kcal

- Carbs: 28g
- Fat: 12g
- Protein: 11g

39. Non-dairy Coconut Milk Yogurt (Homemade)

Preparation Time: 10 minutes

Cooking Time: 24-48 hours

Servings: 4

Ingredients:

- 14 oz. of full-fat coconut milk
- 1/8 tsp. of sea salt
- 1/2 tsp. of maple syrup, pure
- 2 probiotic capsules
- 2 scoops of unflavored collagen peptides

Directions:

1. Sterilize the glass jar that will hold the yogurt by submerging in boiling water.
2. Add the coconut milk to the sterile glass jar and stir.
3. Sprinkle the contents of the probiotic capsules into the coconut milk and stir vigorously.

4. Close the lid of the jar and allow the mixture to ferment for 24-48hours. Shake occasionally to aid the fermentation process.

5. After 24-48 hours, refrigerate the mixture. This is done to thicken the mixture.

6. Stir in the collagen peptides, maple syrup, and sea salt when ready to serve.

7. The mixture must be stored in a refrigerator and consumed within 7 days.

Nutrition:

- Calories: 244 kcal
- Carbs: 18.2g
- Fat: 23g
- Protein: 14g

40. Shamrock Shake

Preparation Time: 10 minutes

Cooking Time: 10 minutes

Servings: 2

Ingredients:

- 1 cup of packed baby spinach
- 2 frozen bananas
- 1/2 avocado, scooped and pitted

- 1/4 cup of mint leaves, fresh
- 1 tsp. of vanilla extract, pure
- 1 cup of homemade hemp seed milk.
- Plant-based whipped cream, optional and as desired
- Vegan chocolate chips, optional and as desired

Directions:

1. Blend the bananas, avocado, spinach, mint leaves, hemp seed milk, and vanilla extract together until smooth and creamy. This may take about 60-90 seconds.
2. The drink is ready to be served. You can top with whipped cream and chocolate chips as desired

Nutrition:

- Calories: 200 kcal
- Carbs: 33g
- Fat: 10g
- Protein: 3g

Chapter 12. Top Superfood Recipes for the Brain

41. Frozen Berry Yogurt

Preparation Time: 10 Minutes

Cooking Time: 10 Minutes

Servings: 2

Ingredients:

- 2 cups of frozen mixed berries, divided
- 1 cup of vanilla low-fat frozen yoghurt, divided
- 1/4 cup of fat-free milk
- 1 tablespoon of chopped fresh mint
- 1 tablespoon of agave syrup

Directions:

1. Mix 1 cup of berries with 3/4 cup yogurt and add the milk, mint, and agave syrup to the food processor.
2. Pulse until smooth.
3. Transfer into a freezer-safe container.
4. Add the remaining one-cup of berries and the remaining 1/4 cup yogurt to the processor; again, pulse until smooth.
5. Drip and swirl the berry mixture into the yogurt mixture.
6. Serve immediately or freeze until firm.

Nutrition:

- Calories: 150kcal
- Fat: 2.5g
- Sat. fat 1.3g
- Protein: 6g
- Carbohydrate: 29g
- Sugar: 13 g
- Fiber: 2g
- Cholesterol: 33mg
- Sodium: 34mg
- Calcium: 155mg

42. Baked Salmon

Preparation Time: 15 Minutes

Cooking Time: 20 Minutes

Servings: 4

Ingredients:

- 2 pounds of salmon, I used Atlantic salmon
- 2 Tablespoons of olive oil

- 3 garlic cloves, minced
- ¼ cup of brown sugar
- ¼ cup of soy sauce
- ½ teaspoon of pepper
- juice of one lemon
- 1 teaspoon of salt
- Sliced lemons and chopped parsley for garnish

Directions:

1. Preheat the oven to 350 °F.
2. Use a baking pan and line it with aluminum foil. Place the salmon on top and sprinkle with salt and pepper to season.
3. Fold the aluminum foil around the salmon fish.
4. In a suitable sized bowl, mix together the olive oil, soy sauce, garlic, brown sugar, lemon juice, salt, and pepper.
5. Pour the prepared seasoning liquid glaze over the salmon and seal the aluminum foil.
6. Bake the salmon for 20-25 minutes.
7. Dip the salmon in the remaining sauce.
8. Garnish it with lemon slices and chopped parsley if desired.

Nutrition:

- Calories 280 Kcal
- Fat 3.1

- Carbohydrates 13g
- Sugar 6g
- Fiber 3g
- Protein 12g
- Cholesterol 0 Mg
- Sodium 119 Mg
- Calcium 4.2 %

43. Avocado Egg Nests

Preparation Time: 10 Minutes

Cooking Time: 10 Minutes

Servings: 4

Ingredients:

- 3 zucchinis, spiralized into noodles
- 2 tablespoons of extra-virgin olive oil
- 4 large eggs
- Kosher salt and freshly ground black pepper
- 2 avocados, halved and thinly sliced
- Red-pepper flakes, for garnishing
- Fresh basil for garnishing.

Directions:

1. Lightly grease a suitable baking sheet and Preheat the oven to 350 °F.
2. In a suitable bowl, combine the zucchini noodles with olive oil and season with salt and pepper to taste.
3. Divide the noodles into 4 equal portions.
4. Move to the baking sheet and shape each bundle into a nest.
5. Crack an egg in the center of each avocado nest.
6. Bake for 9 to 11 minutes.
7. Season with salt and pepper to taste.
8. You can garnish with any choice, such as red pepper flakes and basil.
9. Serve with the baked avocado slices.

Nutrition:

- Calories: 633kcal
- Total Fat: 53g
- Saturated: 3 g
- Carbohydrates: 27g
- Protein: 20g
- Sugars: 9g
- Fiber: 10 g
- Sodium: 113 ₃ Mg Calcium: 8%

44. Super Green Tea Smoothie

Preparation Time: 20 Minutes

Cooking Time: 10 Minutes

Servings: 4

Ingredients:

- 1 cup of brewed green tea chilled
- 1 cup of fresh spinach leaves
- 1 kiwi, peeled
- 1/4 avocado
- 1 banana, broken into chunks and frozen
- 1/2 teaspoon of grated fresh ginger

Directions:

1. Add the tea, spinach, kiwi, banana, avocado, and ginger in a blender.
2. Blend until you get a smooth liquid.

Nutrition:

- Calories: 120kcal
- Total fat: 4.1 g
- Saturated: 0
- Carbohydrates: 22 g
- Sugar: 6 g

- Fiber: 2g
- Protein: 2g
- Cholesterol: 0 mg
- Sodium: 19 mg

45. Dark Chocolate Cake

Preparation Time: 20 Minutes

Cooking Time: 20 Minutes

Servings: 12

Ingredients:

- 2 cups of boiling water
- 1 cup of unsweetened cocoa powder
- 2 3/4 cups of all-purpose flour
- 2 teaspoons of baking soda
- 1/2 teaspoon of baking powder
- 1/2 teaspoon of salt
- 1 cup of butter, softened
- 2 1/4 cups of white sugar
- 4 eggs
- 1 1/2 teaspoons of vanilla extract

Directions:

1. Let the oven heat to 350 ° F and prepare 3 - 9 inch round cake pans by greasing them.

2. In a suitable bowl, pour boiling water into the cocoa and whisk it until you get a smooth mixture.

3. In another medium bowl, add the flour, baking powder, baking soda, and salt and set it aside.

4. In another large bowl, add the cream butter and sugar whisk together until you get a light and fluffy texture.

5. Beat in the eggs one by one, and next, add the vanilla.

6. Combine the flour mixture alternately with the cocoa mixture to the large bowl and whisk to get an even batter.

7. Spread the batter equally between the three greased pans.

8. Bake in the preheated oven for 25 to 30 minutes

9. Allow it to cool; you may decorate as desired.

Nutrition:

- Calories 427kcal
- Fat 18.3
- Carbohydrates 63.8
- Sugar 43 g
- Fiber 10 g
- Protein 6.6g
- Cholesterol 103g, Sodium 465g

Chapter 13. Top Superfood Recipes for Thyroid Health

46. Soy Slow Cooked Ribs with Snap Peas

Preparation Time: 8 Hours

Cooking Time: 30 Minutes

Servings: 5

Ingredients:

- 1 medium onion, sliced
- 1/4 cup of rice vinegar
- 4 cloves garlic, peeled and crushed
- 1/4 cup of low-sodium soy sauce
- 2 tablespoons of light brown sugar
- 1 teaspoon of crushed red pepper
- 2 tablespoons of chopped fresh ginger
- 3 pounds of short ribs
- 2 cups of white rice
- 1/2-pound of snap peas, sliced

Directions:

1. Mix the onion, garlic, vinegar, ginger, soy sauce, sugar, red pepper with ¼-cup of water and add it to a suitable quart slow cooker.

2. Insert the beef in the mix and turn it to allow it to coat with the seasoning.

3. Insert the lid and cook until you feel the beef has become very tender. Do this on low heat for around 7 to 8 hours or on high heat for about 5 to 6 hours (this will shorten total recipe time). Skim off and discard most of the fat.

4. Before serving, cook and prepare the rice as per the package instructions.

5. Serve your slow-cooked tender soy beef over your rice. You can sprinkle sliced snap peas.

Nutrition:

- Calories: 621kcal
- Fat: 23g
- Sat Fat: 10g
- Cholesterol: 134mg
- Sodium: 416mg
- Protein: 48g
- Carbohydrate: 50g
- Sugar: 7g
- Fiber: 3g, Calcium: 60mg

47. Cauliflower Rice with Sautéed Peppers and Onions

Preparation Time: 15 Minutes

Cooking Time: 15 Minutes

Servings: 4

Ingredients:

- 1 head of cauliflower
- 2 green onions and fresh herbs of your choice, finely chopped
- 1 tablespoon of olive oil
- Kosher salt and black pepper to taste
- 1/2 of finely chopped bell pepper

Directions:

1. Prepare the cauliflower head by removing the leaves and separate the tough inner core using a sharp knife to make roughly chopped florets.

2. Add to food processor and pulse until you get a rice-like consistency. You can cook all of it or freeze some for later.

3. Over medium heat, in a suitable skillet, heat oil and sauté the chopped bell peppers and onions for few minutes.

4. Add the cauliflower and stir well, then cover. Every once in a while, let the moisture out.

5. Let it cook for up to 5 minutes or until you feel that the cauliflower is tender and does not taste raw.

Nutrition:

- Calories: 820 kcal
- Fat: 5g
- Sat Fat: 1g
- Cholesterol: 1 mg
- Sodium: 200 mg
- Protein: 12 g
- Carbohydrate: 20 g
- Sugar: 7g
- Fiber: 13 g
- Calcium: 12%

Chapter 14. Side Dishes and Desserts

48. Green Juice Popsicles

Preparation Time: 6 hours+

Cooking Time: 0 minutes

Servings: 6-8

Ingredients:

- 2 large apples, green
- 2 cups of spinach, chopped
- 1 cup of pineapple, diced
- 1 lime, sliced and deseeded
- 1 large green cucumber

Directions:

1. Juice the pineapple, apple, spinach, cucumber, and lime by blending.
2. Once smooth, pour the juice into popsicle molds or ice cube trays until they are ¾ full.
3. Freeze for 30 minutes, then insert the popsicle sticks.
4. Freeze overnight or for about 6 hours until the popsicle is frozen solid.

Nutrition:

- Calories: 42 kcal

- Carbs: 11g
- Fat: 0g
- Protein: 1g

49. Brazil Nut Brownies

Preparation Time: 30 minutes

Cooking Time: 30 minutes

Servings: 9

Ingredients:

- Nonstick cooking spray
- 1/3 cup of honey
- 2 large eggs
- 1 tsp. of salt
- 1/2 cup of sweet cherries, dried
- 1/3 cup of Brazil nuts, chopped
- 1/4 cup of coconut oil
- 2 tsp. of granulated sugar
- 1 tsp. of vanilla extract
- 1/2 gluten-free baking flour
- 1/2 cup 2% of plain yogurt

- 1/3 cup of dark chocolate cocoa powder, unsweetened
- 1/2 tsp. of baking powder

Directions:

1. Preheat the oven to 375 °F, place the rack in the middle of the oven and coat the baking pan with nonstick spray.
2. In a large bowl, mix the sugar, oil, and honey. Beat until well blended. Add in the eggs and vanilla extract and keep beating. When well combined, add the yogurt and beat until the batter becomes smooth.
3. In another large bowl, mix the flour, baking powder, cocoa powder, and salt.
4. While beating continuously, add the flour mixture to the egg mixture and keep beating until the batter is well combined.
5. Add in the Brazil nuts and stir.
6. Pour the batter on the prepared baking pan. Arrange the cherries on the batter, taking into consideration how the cherries will be positioned when the brownie is divided into squares.
7. Bake until the brownies are set. This may take up to 20 minutes. When ready, remove the baking pan from the oven and allow it to cool for 5 minutes.
8. Cut the brownies into square pieces and serve.

Nutrition:

- Calories: 240 kcal
- Carbs: 33g
- Fat: 25g, Protein: 4g

50. Banana Sushi

Preparation Time: 10 minutes

Cooking Time: 0 minutes

Servings: 2

Ingredients:

- 1 large banana
- 1 Tbsps. of hemp seed cream cheese
- 1 Tbsps. of hemp seeds
- 1/2 cup of granola
- 1 tsp. of chocolate chips

Directions:

1. Get a plastic bag, add the granola, chocolate chips, hemp seeds, then push all the air out and seal tight.
2. With a rolling pin, crush all the cereal within the plastic bag into pieces.
3. Peel the banana and coat it completely with hemp seed cream cheese.
4. Open the plastic bag and pour the contents on a chopping board.
5. Roll the coated banana over the chopping board's cereals and gently press to ensure the cereals stick without squishing the banana.
6. Divide the banana into two equal pieces and serve.

Nutrition:

- Calories: 67.5 kcal
- Carbs: 10.2g
- Fat: 2.3g
- Protein: 1.9g

51. Mango Fruit Tart

Preparation Time: 20 minutes

Cooking Time: 15 minutes

Servings: 10

Ingredients:

Tart Crust:

- 15 Medjool dates, pitted and dried.
- 3/4 cup of cashews, raw and unsalted
- 2 Tbsps. of unsweetened coconut flakes, shredded
- 1 Tbsps. of melted coconut oil

Mango Cream:

- 3/4 cup of coconut milk yogurt, homemade
- 3/4 cup of fresh mango, sliced

Toppings:

- 1 cup of mango, diced
- 1/2 cup of raspberries
- 1/2 cup of blackberries
- 1/2 cup of blueberries

Mango Glaze:

- 1 Tbsps. of mango preServings
- 1 tsp. of water

Directions:

1. Preheat the oven to 350 °F.
2. Blend the Medjool dates, coconut flakes, cashew nuts, and coconut oil in a food processor until a fine consistency is obtained.
3. Coat the date blend on the outside and bottom side of a tart tin pan, then bake for about 15 minutes. Remove from oven and allow to cool before removing the crust from the tart tin.
4. Blend the yogurt and mango in either a food processor or a blender. Once smooth, pour it into date crust and refrigerate until it is set. This may take about 20 minutes.
5. For toppings, add the diced mango, raspberries, blackberries, and blueberries.
6. Mix the mango preServings and water in a small bowl, microwave for 25 seconds, and stir to make the glaze.
7. Brush the glaze over the mango tart and serve.

Nutrition:

- Calories: 18 kcal
- Carbs: -g
- Fat: -g,
- Protein: -g

CPSIA information can be obtained
at www.ICGtesting.com
Printed in the USA
BVHW061306310321
603631BV00018B/322